CANADIAN CURRICULUM PRESS
Forward Learning

Reading

Grade 1

P9-BIF-960

Table of Contents

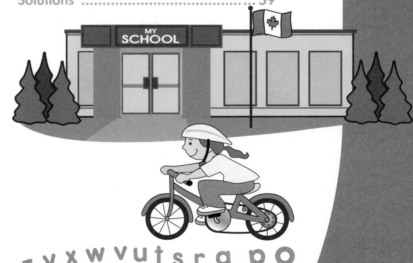

z y x w v u t s r q p o

a b c d e f g h i j k l m n

- Letter sounds, sight words
- Vowel sounds, plurals
- Picture clues, rhyming
- Reading comprehension activities
- And much more!

D. J. Whitlock, B.Ed.

Letters, Sounds, and Words

Initial Sounds

Initial sounds are what we hear at the beginning of words.
Say each letter. Say the sound each letter makes.
Circle the letter that make the initial sound for each picture.

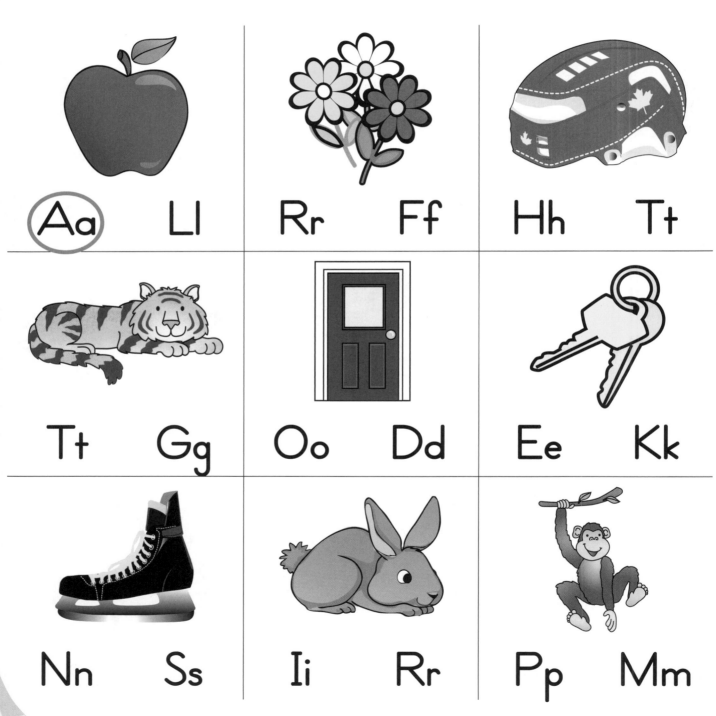

(Aa) Ll	Rr Ff	Hh Tt
Tt Gg	Oo Dd	Ee Kk
Nn Ss	Ii Rr	Pp Mm

Initial Sounds

Look at each picture. Write the letter that makes the initial sound for each picture.

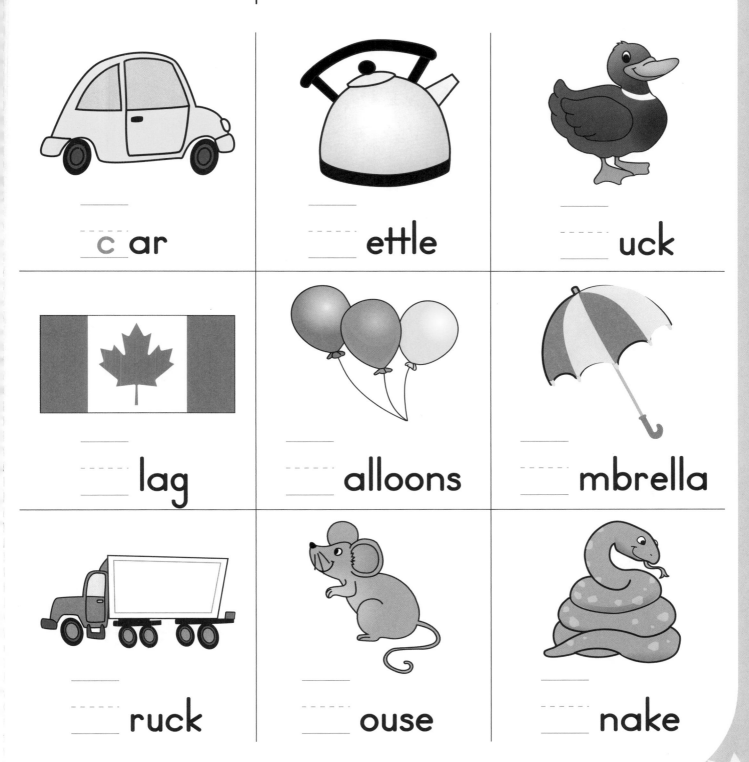

c ar

_____ ettle

_____ uck

_____ lag

_____ alloons

_____ mbrella

_____ ruck

_____ ouse

_____ nake

Final Sounds

Final sounds are what we hear at the **end** of words.
Look at each picture. Write the letter that makes the
final sound for each picture.

ice crea m   bal ___   hamburge ___

boo ___   carro ___   yo-y ___

be ___   octopu ___   trai ___

Scrambled Letters

Unscramble the word. Write the word on the line.

n a f

fan

i g p

_____

- - - - - - - - - -

_____

r c a

_____

- - - - - - - - - -

_____

g b u

_____

- - - - - - - - - -

_____

t a b

_____

- - - - - - - - - -

_____

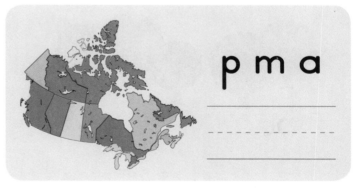

p m a

_____

- - - - - - - - - -

_____

10

t n e

_____

- - - - - - - - - -

_____

a c t

_____

- - - - - - - - - -

_____

Plurals

Words that refer to more than one of something are plurals.
Look at the pictures. Write the plural words.
Use the Plural Word List if you need help.

Plural Word List

dogs   balls   apples   crayons   trees   frogs

apples

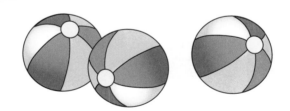

Picture Clues

Pictures help you!
Read the sentence. Circle the word that makes sense. Then, write the word.

Mom is at the _____ **park** .

(park)   plant

I ride in a _____ .

car   cat

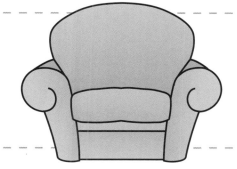

I sit on a _____ .

sofa   chair

I ride in a _____ .

bus   box

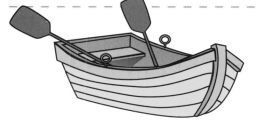

Dad has a _____ .

bike   boat

Sight Words

Learning sight words makes reading easier. Practice these sight words with an adult.

Note to Parents
Children will learn to recognize sight words quickly. This will help them read with accuracy and fluency.

the	or	by	up	no
is	of	that	but	like
in	and	was	not	my
it	a	are	can	what
to	you	with	said	were
I	see	they	an	when
he	for	this	she	come
at	on	saw	do	have
be	as	had	so	some
we	his	all	look	into

there		came
if		down
go		them
will		would
out		could
then		went
yes		her
make		am
little		get
here		want

Letters, Sounds, and Words

Sight Words

Unscramble these sight words. Write them correctly. Use the Sight Word Bank to help.

Sight Word Bank

at
will
by
is
you
be
was
this
they
said
for
come

si	ouy	yeht
is		
eb	swa	yb
rof	liwl	meco
siht	ta	iads

9

Sight Word Search

Find and circle the sight words in the puzzle.
Words are across or down.

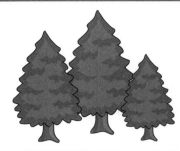

a	b	l	i	g	k	j	w	t	b	h	a	v	e	a
l	k	w	f	i	n	t	o	c	v	s	m	s	o	y
i	p	r	g	b	l	x	c	l	n	a	n	a	x	e
t	d	a	j	v	p	t	t	h	a	t	r	i	t	s
t	f	l	d	q	z	l	o	w	n	l	o	d	o	t
l	r	l	e	d	e	n	s	q	d	v	p	s	o	v
e	t	v	w	t	h	e	a	z	r	e	w	h	e	n
y	l	o	o	k	e	m	l	i	k	e	r	j	n	i

Find these words:

| look | like | little | all | said | have |
| that | when | and | into | the | yes |

10

Picture Clues and Sight Words

Practice Reading with Picture Clues and Sight Words

Use the pictures to help you read the sentences.
The sight words have been underlined.
Sound out the words. Practice reading each sentence.

The boy is in the wagon.

The frog is on the log.

The sheep was at the barn.

He has a green hat and red shoes.

Picture Clues and Sight Words

Picture Match

Match each sentence to the picture.
Underline the sight words in the sentence.

<u>The</u> girl <u>is</u> <u>in</u> <u>the</u> bathtub.

The girl is on the beach.

The girl is at school.

The girl is riding her bike.

The girl is in the kitchen.

The girl is at a party.

More Picture Clues

Can You Find the Match?

Match each picture to the words that make sense.
The first one is done for you.

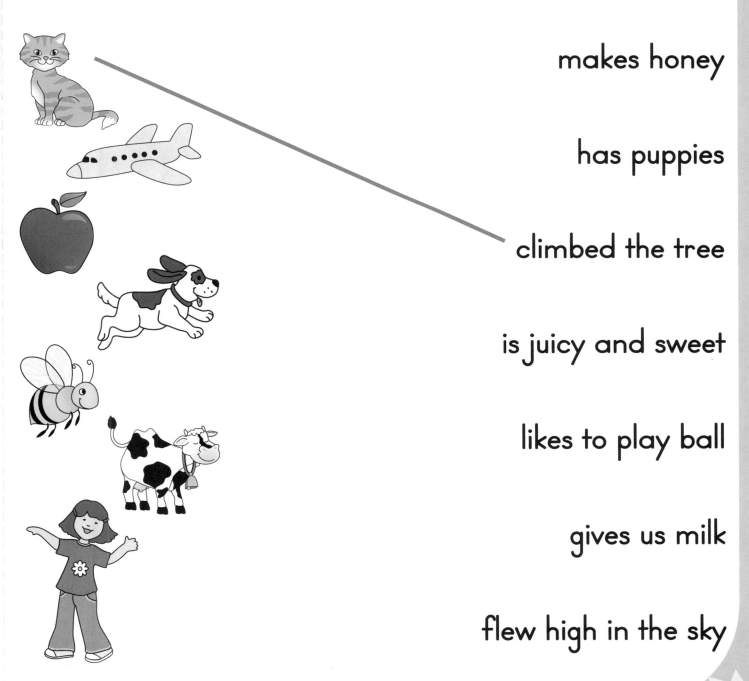

makes honey

has puppies

climbed the tree

is juicy and sweet

likes to play ball

gives us milk

flew high in the sky

Colour Clues

Read each sentence. Find the word in the Word Bank that makes sense. Print the word on the line.

Word Bank

yellow   black   red   green   blue   purple   orange   white

He wore _____ jeans to school.

The stop sign was bright _____.

Spring leaves on the tree are _____.

Nice puffy _____ clouds are in the sky.

The boy put _____ mustard on his hotdog.

The sky was _____ at night.

She put _____ grape jelly on her bread.

At Halloween the _____ pumpkin was ready to cut.

14

Rhyming

Rhyming Words

Read each sentence. Do you hear the two rhyming words?
Underline the words that rhyme.

The <u>hat</u> was on the <u>cat</u>.

I can bake a cake.

She ate a bun in the sun.

There is a bug on the rug.

The pig is wearing a wig.

The frog jumped on a log.

Rhyming

More Rhyming Words

Fill in the blanks with words that rhyme with the underlined word. Use the pictures as clues.

The ___man___ drove a delivery <u>van</u>.

The boy hit his <u>head</u> _____ when he fell off the _____ .

After <u>school</u>, _____ I swam in the _____ .

With my _____ , I print the number <u>ten</u>.

I skinned my _____ climbing a <u>tree</u>.

Detail Words

Who or What?

Detail Words like "who" or "what" provide information.
The circled words tell us "who" or "what." Print "who"
or "what" on each line.

(My dad) is at home.   **who**

Children love to eat (candy.) _____

The girl got new (shoes.) _____

The (magician) did neat tricks. _____

(Farrah and her friend) went to the park. _____

(The car) drove on the road. _____

(The bird) flew to the tree. _____

Letters, Sounds, and Words

Detail Words

When or Where?

Detail Words like "when" or "where" provide information. The circled words tell us "when" or "where." Print "when" or "where" on each line.

On (Halloween,) I get candy.  when

The milk is (in the fridge.) _____

(Tomorrow,) we go to school. _____

The pig rolled (in the mud.) _____

The hat is (on his head.) _____

In (December,) it will snow. _____

On (Monday,) I go swimming. _____

Nouns - People

Community Helpers

Community helpers are people who do jobs that help others. Draw a line to connect each sentence with the correct community helper.

I help students read and do math.

I put out fires.

I deliver mail.

I tend to people when they are sick.

I keep people safe.

I take care of animals.

I look at your teeth.

Nouns - Objects

Pick an Object

Read the sentences. Look at the pictures. Print the sentence number in the box to show which object goes with each sentence.

1. Print your name with this.
2. Eat ice cream with this.
3. Cut paper with this.
4. Boil water in this.

5. Watch your favourite show on this.
6. Make your hair neat with this.
7. Cut an apple with this.
8. Put in a nail with this.

Closed Questions

Yes or No

Questions that can be answered with
yes or no are closed questions.
Read each question. Is the answer yes or no?
Circle your answer.

Can a bird fly? (yes) no

Is an apple a vegetable?   yes   no

Is a puppy a baby dog? yes   no

Is it cold in the winter?   yes   no

Will it snow in the summer?   yes   no

Is chocolate a healthy snack?   yes   no

Can a lion eat a mouse?   yes   no

Is grass orange?   yes   no

Do fish swim in water?   yes   no

Do cars drive on the road?   yes   no

Sentences

Choose the Best Sentence

Read each sentence. Select the sentence that **best describes** the picture. Underline the sentence.

The toys are a mess.

Dad put the toys away.

<u>The teddy bear, clown, and car are in the toy box.</u>

- -

The girl is going to school.

The girl loves the bath.

The girl is going to bed.

- -

The boy is going swimming.

The boy is playing in the sand.

The boy has a ball.

Sentences

Picture Match

Look at each picture. Read each sentence.
Match each sentence with the best picture.

This keeps you warm.

This protects you from the sun.

This is a sport cap.

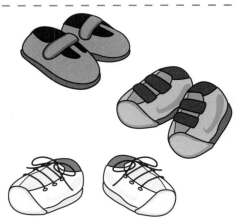

These have Velcro.

These have laces.

These are blue.

This ball is for kicking.

This ball is for hitting with a bat.

This ball is for playing in a pool.

Sentences

Choose the Best Sentence

Look at each picture. Read each sentence. Draw a line from the picture to the sentence that **best describes** the picture.

The loon is flying.

The loon swims in the lake. ———————

The loon is on the shore.

The bike has 2 wheels.

The bike goes fast.

The girl is on the bike.

Ice cream is a cool treat.

The cake is chocolate.

The dog is barking.

It is breakfast time.

The pancakes have syrup on them.

I am hungry.

Sentences

Choose the Best Sentence

Look at each picture. Read each sentence. Draw a line from the picture to the sentence that **best describes** the picture.

Fruit is healthy.

Cupcakes are good.

I had chicken for lunch.

An octopus has eight legs.

Fish swim in water.

Octopus eat fish.

Strawberries grow in trees.

I had ice cream for dessert.

Strawberries are a fruit.

The giraffe swims.

Two giraffes sleep.

The giraffe has a long neck.

Paragraphs and Titles

Choose the Best Title

Read each paragraph. Read the three titles. Underline the title that best describes the paragraph.

Sarah put on her blue bathing suit. She walked to the pool. Then she jumped in the water and made a splash.

<u>Swimming</u>

Sarah Likes to Play

A Hot Day

A dog can run. Monkeys can run too. But a cheetah is the fastest runner of all!

Run

Animals That Run

Running Dogs

Spread out the dough. Add some sauce and cheese. Put the pizza in the oven. Enjoy!

Making a Pizza

Baking

Food

Mohamed puts his skates on. He grabs his stick and a puck. Then he goes on the ice and scores a goal.

Skating

Cold Winter

Mohamed Plays Hockey

Following Directions

Picture Perfect

Read the sentences. Draw a picture to explain the words.

The circle is smaller than
the square.

Two balloons are red.
One balloon is blue.

The yellow flower is in
the green grass.

The tree has red apples.

Following Directions

More Picture Perfect

Read the sentences. Follow the instructions.

Colour the house blue.
Draw 3 flowers beside the house.

Colour the shoe red.
Draw a soccer ball beside it.

Colour the duck yellow.
Draw a duckling beside it.

Colour the car green.
Draw a brown dog beside it.

Picture Clues

Reading with Picture Clues

Read the story. Use the pictures to help you.
Answer the questions.

Brad brushed his teeth.

He put his pyjamas on.

He read a book.

Brad kissed his mom.

He turned out the light.

 the answer.

Who did Brad kiss?	What did Brad do?
dad mom	read a book watched TV

What did Brad put on?	Where was Brad going?
shoes pyjamas	to bed to school

Lists

Reading a List

Read. Answer the questions.

milk

eggs

bread

apples

bananas

sugar

cheese

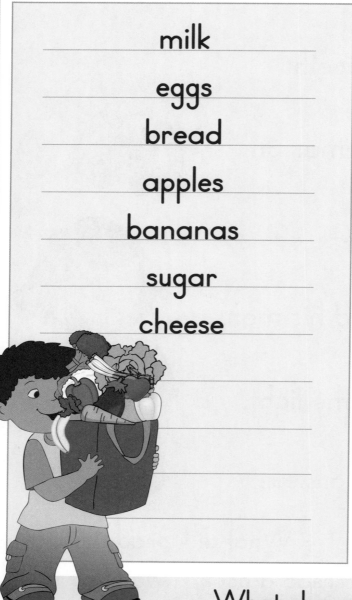

Circle the answer.

What kind of writing is this?
a letter   a list

How many items are there?
7   9

How many fruits are there?
3   2

Are chips one of the words?
yes   no

What else might you add?

_____

- -

Notes

Reading a Note

Read. Answer the questions.

Dad,
I am on my bike. I went to the school.
Ali and Jared are with me.
        Back soon,
            Sarah

Circle the answer.

| What kind of writing is this? | Did they walk to the school? |
| invitation   note | yes   no |

How many people went bike riding?
2   3

Who wrote the note?
Sarah   Dad

What else could you add to the note?

_____

_____

Invitations

Reading an Invitation

Read. Look at the picture.
Answer the questions.

Party Celebration!

What: Zahra's 8th
birthday party
Where: Community Pool
Date: August 10
Time: 1:00 pm

Circle the answer.

What kind of party is it?
Mother's Day   birthday

Who is the party for?
Malik   Zahra

What date is the party on?
1:00 pm   August 10

How old is Zahra?
6 years old   8 years old

What would you take to the party besides a present?

_____

_____

_____

Boxes

Reading a Box

Read. Look at the picture.
Answer the questions.

Underline the right answer.

What is this box advertising?
bird food   dog food

- - - - - - - - - - - - - - - - - - - -

How often should a bird be fed?

twice a day

once a day

- - - - - - - - - - - - - - - - - - - -

A parrot is what type of animal?
bird   snake

What else does a bird need to survive?

33

Comic Strips

The Lemonade Stand

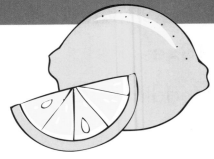

Read. Look at the pictures. Answer the questions.

Underline the right answer.

What form of writing is this?

poem   comic

How much did the lemonade cost?

25¢   10¢

How many glasses of lemonade were sold?

five   eight

What might the child do with the money?

Poetry

Reading Poetry

Read. Look at the pictures. Answer the questions.

In the winter, we wait
for snow,
Then it's off to the hill we go,

We walk up with our sled
and a hat on our head,

Down the hill we slide,
For a quick and snowy ride.

Underline the right answer.

What form of writing is this?
poem   story

- - - - - - - - - - - - - - - - - - -

What is this writing about?
skating   tobogganing

- - - - - - - - - - - - - - - - - - -

Which word rhymes
with slide?
ride   head

- - - - - - - - - - - - - - - - - - -

Which word rhymes
with go?
sled   snow

Riddles

Reading Riddles

Read. Look at the pictures. Answer the questions

What Am I?

I stand there waiting
day and night.
My string net hangs from
my hoop.
I wait for orange balls to
be tossed my way.

What am I?

Circle the right answer.

What form of writing is this?
poem   riddle

- - - - - - - - - - - - - - - -

What is this writing about?
a basketball   a basketball net

- - - - - - - - - - - - - - - -

What hangs from me?
wooden net   string net

- - - - - - - - - - - - - - - -

What do I wait to be tossed
my way?
yellow balls   orange balls

Finding Details

Look for Details

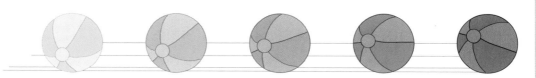

Read. Look at the pictures. Complete the sentences.

My Bouncy Ball

My ball can bounce.
It may roll away, but I will get it.
My ball is red and blue.
I like to play ball with my friends.

Fill in the blanks.

The _____ can bounce.

The colours of the ball are _____ and _____.

I like to play with my _____.

My ball may _____ away.

Story Sequence

What Happened First, Next, Then, and Last

Look at the pictures. Print the number 1, 2, 3, or 4 in the box to put them in order. The first one is started.

Story Sequence

Order of Steps

Read the steps.
Look at the pictures.
Write the numbers
1, 2, 3, or 4 in
each circle to show
the steps.

How to Make a Chocolate Sundae!

What You Need:
ice cream, chocolate sauce, whipped cream,
cherry, bowl, scoop, spoon

Steps:
1. Scoop ice cream into a bowl.
2. Pour some chocolate sauce on top of the ice cream.
3. Put some whipped cream on the chocolate sauce.
4. Put a cherry on top.
5. Eat and enjoy!

Picture Clues

What's Missing?

Look at the paragraph. Print the missing initial letters in the blanks. Use the Picture Word Bank to help you. Read the completed paragraph.

The Zoo
_____

We went to the zoo. I saw ____iraffes, ____heetahs, and many ____onkeys. A ____ookeeper takes care of the animals. She feeds the ____olar bears ____ish. The animals sleep in the ____un. It is fun to go to the ____oo.

Picture Word Bank

polar bear

giraffe

zookeeper

sun

monkey

cheetah

fish

zoo

Picture Clues

Read the Story to Find Details

First, read the story. Then read the questions. (Circle) the correct picture to answer each question. Last, colour the pictures.

Making Cookies

My mom made some cookies. She put them in the oven to bake. They smelled good. I ate two cookies and they were yummy.

What was baked?	Who baked them?	Where were they baked?

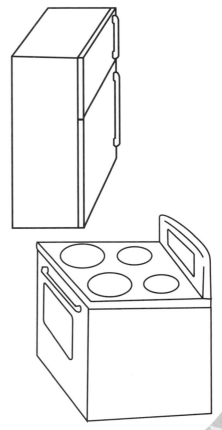

Following Directions

Drawing a Butterfly

Read the steps. Follow the steps to draw the butterfly in the box.

1. Draw an oval for the body.

2. Add a circle on top of the oval for the head.

3. Draw a backward "B" on the left side of the oval for one wing.

4. Draw a proper "B" on the right side of the oval for another wing.

5. Put two antennae on the head.

6. Add eyes and a mouth.

7. Colour your butterfly.

Book Covers

Reading the Cover of a Book

A book cover tells:
- Title (idea of what the book is about)
- Author (who wrote the book)
- Illustrator (who drew the pictures)

Look at the book cover.
Answer the questions.

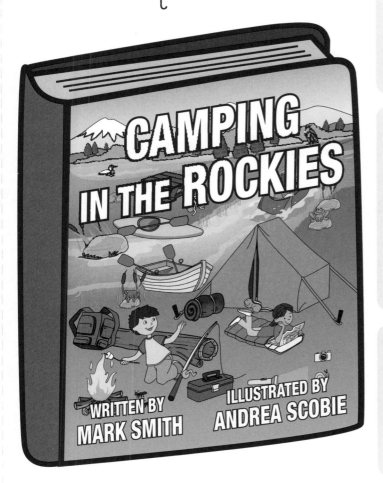

Who wrote this book?

_____

- - - - - - - - - - - - - -

_____

Who drew the pictures
in the book?

_____

- - - - - - - - - - - - - -

_____

What is the book about?

_____

- - - - - - - - - - - - - -

_____

Signs

Reading Neighbourhood Signs

Read. Answer the questions.

LEMONADE STAND

Saturday July 7th
10:00am to noon

homemade lemonade ✳ cookies
candy ✳ surprises

What time does the lemonade sale begin?

How long is the stand open?

On what day will the stand be open?

What kinds of things can you buy at the lemonade stand?

What might a "surprise" be?

Story Order

Read the story.

Swimming Lessons

Today was my first swimming lesson. We walked to the pool. I put my bathing suit on. I met my teacher. We jumped in the water. It was fun!

Rewrite the sentences below in the correct order.

I put my bathing suit on.	We walked to the pool.
We jumped in the water.	I met my teacher.

1. _____

2. _____

3. _____

4. _____

Story Order

Read the story.

Henry's Birthday

Henry's birthday party is today. He is 6 years old. First, he and his pals played games. Then they had pizza and cupcakes for lunch. Last, they sang "Happy Birthday."

Rewrite the sentences below in the correct order.

Last, they sang "Happy Birthday."

First, they played games.

Today is Henry's birthday.   Then they had lunch.

1. _____

2. _____

3. _____

4. _____

Story Details

Finding Story Details

Read the story. Answer the questions.

Friends

My friend Alex and I like to swim after lunch. We go to the lake or pool. We jump in the water, play tag, or have races. Alex likes to blow bubbles. There are many rules to follow when we go swimming. Swimming is excellent exercise.

What is my friend's name?

_____

_____

_____

Where do we like to swim?

_____

_____

_____

What does Alex like to do in the water?

_____

_____

_____

When do we like to swim?

_____

_____

_____

What are some swimming rules?

_____

_____

Character

Describing Characters in a Story

Read the story.
Answer the questions.

Best Friends

Sam and Tara are best friends. They are in the same class. They like the same games. They both love dogs. Both girls have brown hair. Sam has one sister. Tara has two brothers. Sam and Tara play badminton in the gym every Saturday.

What do Sam and Tara both like?

_____

- -

_____

_____

How are the girls different?

_____

- -

_____

_____

What do they do every Saturday?

_____

- -

_____

Visualizing Characters

Best Friends

Draw a picture of Sam and Tara playing badminton.

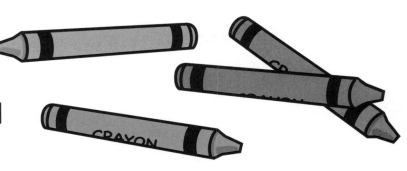

Story Details

Finding Story Details

Read the story. Answer the questions in complete sentences.

> ### Trains
>
> Trains can be long. They go very fast. Some trains carry people.
> Some trains are very loud. Trains ride on tracks.

Are trains fast or slow?

_____

- -

_____

What do some trains carry?

_____

- -

_____

What do trains ride on?

_____

- -

_____

Can you hear a train?

_____

- -

Use of Words

Fun with Words

Read the story. Answer the questions.

Bugs

Small ones, big ones, thin ones, fat ones — bugs are all around. I am frightened and I yell, "Go away!" They creep, slither, and run out of sight. I feel better when I can't see any bugs.

Circle the answer.

In the story, the word "frightened" means:

a. scared   b. happy

c. sad

The opposite of "yell" is:

a. sing   b. whisper

c. squeal

The word "bug" is a:

a. noun   b. verb

The word "can't" means:

a. can   b. cannot

c. could

Which word does **not** rhyme with "run"?

a. bun   b. sun

c. rope

Facts

Pet Fact Cards

There are many kinds of cards. Some are about sports.
These cards are about house pets.

HAMSTER

HOUSEHOLD PETS

The front of the fact card has a picture so we know what the pet looks like.

The back of the card has facts.

HAMSTERS
• Hamsters live in cages. They like tunnels and wheels in their cage.
• Hamsters eat seeds, vegetables, and hamster treats.
• Hamsters are nocturnal. They sleep during the day and are awake at night.

Facts

Finding Facts

Look at the card.
Did you notice the
fish bowl?
Can you see the fins?
Do you see the tail?

Answer the questions.

GOLDFISH
HOUSEHOLD PETS

GOLDFISH
- Goldfish live in a fish bowl or an aquarium.
- There are 500 types of goldfish.
- Goldfish eat flakes of food.
- Goldfish have colourful bodies.
- Goldfish like to live in groups.

What facts did you learn about the goldfish?

Would you like a goldfish for a pet? Why or why not?

Conflict or Problem

Identify the Problem

Read the story. Answer the questions in complete sentences.

Going to the Beach

Tom went to the beach with his friend Samir. They played in the sand with an orange pail. Waves came up on the beach and took the orange pail out into the water. Tom was upset. Samir went into the water to get the bucket. Tom put the bucket far from the waves.

What is the problem or conflict in the story?

_____

- -

_____

- -

_____

How was the problem solved?

_____

- -

_____

- -

_____

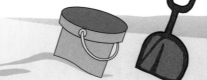

Personal Connection

Making a Connection to the Story

Read the story. Think about a time when you were scared. Answer the questions in complete sentences.

At the Park

Shelby went to the park with her mom. She played on the swings. Her mom pushed her too high. Shelby got scared and started to cry. Shelby's mom stopped the swing and gave her a hug.

What has scared you?

_____

- -

_____

- -

_____

What made you feel better?

_____

- -

_____

- -

_____

```
R F A T E O F A N D
F T F H W E O Y O U
E O W I T H B Y I S
O O I E H T H A T S
T H E O N S E E I T
T N H E I N A R E I
I T E F O R N B E W
R A S D W A S A I O
E S H I S T T O A N
R W A S O R T H E T
```

Find these words:

AND	BE	HIS	OF	THAT	WE
ARE	BY	IN	ON	THE	WITH
AS	FOR	IS	OR	TO	YOU
AT	HE	IT	SEE	WAS	

```
I M Y C O M E A L L
C H A D A S A I D H
N O O L O O K C A N
I N O T W H A T A T
O S H E T H E Y U K
T E I N T O H A V E
M A N B U T H I S O
W H E N W E R E L I L
L T D O S O M E U P
C L I K E E S A W S
```

Find these words:

ALL	COME	INTO	NO	SHE	THIS	WHEN
AN	DO	LIKE	NOT	SO	UP	
BUT	HAD	LOOK	SAID	SOME	WERE	
CAN	HAVE	MY	SAW	THEY	WHAT	

```
A M T H E M C A M E
I E W O U L D E L C
E W Y E S M A K E L
D O W N T H E N N E
E E O U T C O U L D
H E R E W E N T E N
W T T H E R E T T U
D I F W I L L G O O
R H E R L I T T L E
M W A N T G E T E E
```

Find these words:

AM	DOWN	HER	LITTLE	THEM	WANT	WOULD
CAME	GET	HERE	MAKE	THEN	WENT	YES
COULD	GO	IF	OUT	THERE	WILL	

Solutions

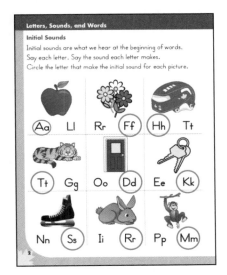

Page 2

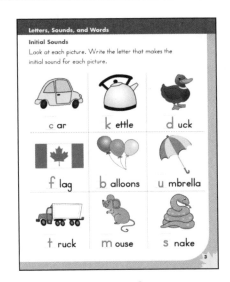

Page 3

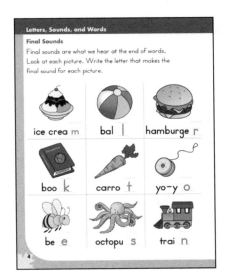

Page 4

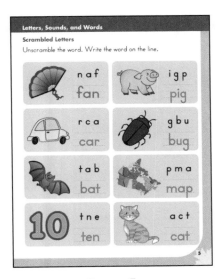

Page 5

Page 6

Page 7

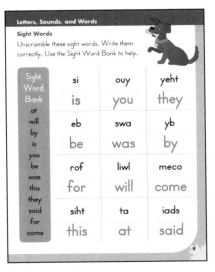

Page 9

Page 10

Page 12

Solutions

Letters, Sounds, and Words
More Picture Clues
Can You Find the Match?

Match each picture to the words that make sense.
The first one is done for you.

- makes honey
- has puppies
- climbed the tree
- is juicy and sweet
- likes to play ball
- gives us milk
- flew high in the sky

Page 13

Letters, Sounds, and Words
Colour Clues
Read each sentence. Find the word in the Word Bank that makes sense. Print the word on the line.

Word Bank
yellow **black** red green blue purple orange **white**

He wore **blue** jeans to school.

The stop sign was bright **red** .

Spring leaves on the tree are **green** .

Nice puffy **white** clouds are in the sky.

The boy put **yellow** mustard on his hotdog.

The sky was **black** at night.

She put **purple** grape jelly on her bread.

At Halloween the **orange** pumpkin was ready to cut.

Page 14

Letters, Sounds, and Words
Rhyming
Rhyming Words

Read each sentence. Do you hear the two rhyming words? Underline the words that rhyme.

The <u>hat</u> was on the <u>cat</u>.

I can <u>bake</u> a <u>cake</u>.

She ate a <u>bun</u> in the <u>sun</u>.

There is a <u>bug</u> on the <u>rug</u>.

The <u>pig</u> is wearing a <u>wig</u>.

The <u>frog</u> jumped on a <u>log</u>.

Page 15

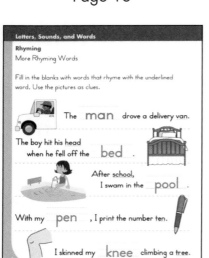

Letters, Sounds, and Words
Rhyming
More Rhyming Words

Fill in the blanks with words that rhyme with the underlined word. Use the pictures as clues.

The **man** drove a delivery van.

The boy hit his head when he fell off the **bed** .

After school, I swam in the **pool** .

With my **pen** , I print the number ten.

I skinned my **knee** climbing a tree.

Page 16

Letters, Sounds, and Words
Detail Words
Who or What?

Detail Words like "who" or "what" provide information.
The circled words tell us "who" or "what." Print "who" or "what" on each line.

(My dad) is at home. **who**

Children love to eat (candy). **what**

The girl got new (shoes). **what**

The (magician) did neat tricks. **who**

(Farrah and her friend) went to the park. **who**

(The car) drove on the road. **what**

(The bird) flew to the tree. **what**

Page 17

Letters, Sounds, and Words
Detail Words
When or Where?

Detail Words like "when" or "where" provide information.
The circled words tell us "when" or "where." Print "when" or "where" on each line.

On (Halloween), I get candy. **when**

The milk is (in the fridge). **where**

(Tomorrow), we go to school. **when**

The pig rolled (in the mud). **where**

The hat is (on his head). **where**

In (December), it will snow. **when**

On (Monday), I go swimming. **when**

Page 18

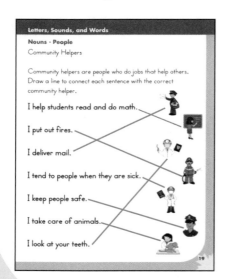

Letters, Sounds, and Words
Nouns - People
Community Helpers

Community helpers are people who do jobs that help others.
Draw a line to connect each sentence with the correct community helper.

I help students read and do math.

I put out fires.

I deliver mail.

I tend to people when they are sick.

I keep people safe.

I take care of animals.

I look at your teeth.

Page 19

Letters, Sounds, and Words
Nouns - Objects
Pick an Object

Read the sentences. Look at the pictures. Print the sentence number in the box to show which object goes with each sentence.

1. Print your name with this.
2. Eat ice cream with this.
3. Cut paper with this.
4. Boil water in this.
5. Watch your favourite show on this.
6. Make your hair neat with this.
7. Cut an apple with this.
8. Put in a nail with this.

3 2 1 7

4 6 5 8

Page 20

Letters, Sounds, and Words
Closed Questions
Yes or No

Questions that can be answered with yes or no are closed questions.
Read each question. Is the answer yes or no? Circle your answer.

Can a bird fly? (yes) no

Is an apple a vegetable? yes (no)

Is a puppy a baby dog? (yes) no

Is it cold in the winter? (yes) no

Will it snow in the summer? yes (no)

Is chocolate a healthy snack? yes (no)

Can a lion eat a mouse? (yes) no

Is grass orange? yes (no)

Do fish swim in water? (yes) no

Do cars drive on the road? (yes) no

Page 21

Solutions

Page 22

Reading Comprehension

Sentences
Choose the Best Sentence

Read each sentence. Select the sentence that best describes the picture. Underline the sentence.

The toys are a mess.
Dad put the toys away.
<u>The teddy bear, clown, and car are in the toy box.</u>

The girl is going to school.
<u>The girl loves the bath.</u>
The girl is going to bed.

The boy is going swimming.
The boy is playing in the sand.
<u>The boy has a ball.</u>

Page 23

Reading Comprehension

Sentences
Picture Match

Look at each picture. Read each sentence. Match each sentence with the best picture.

This keeps you warm.
This protects you from the sun.
This is a sport cap.

These have Velcro.
These have laces.
These are blue.

This ball is for kicking.
This ball is for hitting with a bat.
This ball is for playing in a pool.

Page 24

Reading Comprehension

Sentences
Choose the Best Sentence

Look at each picture. Read each sentence. Draw a line from the picture to the sentence that best describes the picture.

The loon is flying.
The loon swims in the lake.
The loon is on the shore.

The bike has 2 wheels.
The bike goes fast.
The girl is on the bike.

Ice cream is a cool treat.
The cake is chocolate.
The dog is barking.

It is breakfast time.
The pancakes have syrup on them.
I am hungry.

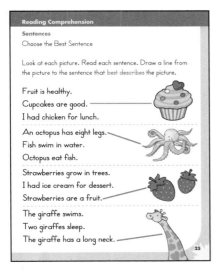

Page 25

Reading Comprehension

Sentences
Choose the Best Sentence

Look at each picture. Read each sentence. Draw a line from the picture to the sentence that best describes the picture.

Fruit is healthy.
Cupcakes are good.
I had chicken for lunch.

An octopus has eight legs.
Fish swim in water.
Octopus eat fish.

Strawberries grow in trees.
I had ice cream for dessert.
Strawberries are a fruit.

The giraffe swims.
Two giraffes sleep.
The giraffe has a long neck.

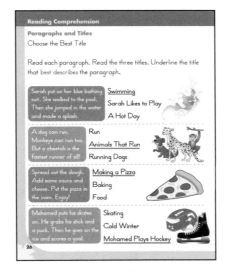

Page 26

Reading Comprehension

Paragraphs and Titles
Choose the Best Title

Read each paragraph. Read the three titles. Underline the title that best describes the paragraph.

Sarah put on her blue bathing suit. She walked to the pool. Then she jumped in the water and made a splash.
<u>Swimming</u>
Sarah Likes to Play
A Hot Day

A dog can run. Monkeys can run too. But a cheetah is the fastest runner of all!
Run
<u>Animals That Run</u>
Running Dogs

Spread out the dough. Add some sauce and cheese. Put the pizza in the oven. Enjoy!
<u>Making a Pizza</u>
Baking
Food

Mohamed puts his skates on. He grabs his stick and a puck. Then he goes on the ice and scores a goal.
Skating
Cold Winter
<u>Mohamed Plays Hockey</u>

Page 27

Reading Comprehension

Following Directions
Picture Perfect

Read the sentences. Draw a picture to explain the words.

The circle is smaller than the square.

Two balloons are red. One balloon is blue.

The yellow flower is in the green grass.

The tree has red apples.

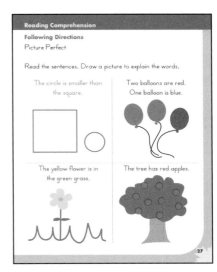

Page 28

Reading Comprehension

Following Directions
More Picture Perfect

Read the sentences. Follow the instructions.

Colour the house blue.
Draw 3 flowers beside the house.

Colour the shoe red.
Draw a soccer ball beside it.

Colour the duck yellow.
Draw a duckling beside it.

Colour the car green.
Draw a brown dog beside it.

Page 29

Reading Comprehension

Picture Clues
Reading with Picture Clues

Read the story. Use the pictures to help you. Answer the questions.

Brad brushed his teeth.
He put his pyjamas on.
He read a book.
Brad kissed his mom.
He turned out the light.

Circle the answer.

Who did Brad kiss?
dad (mom)

What did Brad do?
(read a book) watched TV

What did Brad put on?
shoes (pyjamas)

Where was Brad going?
(to bed) to school

Page 30

Reading Comprehension

Lists
Reading a List

Read. Answer the questions.

milk
eggs
bread
apples
bananas
sugar
cheese

Circle the answer.

What kind of writing is this?
a letter (a list)

How many items are there?
(7) 9

How many fruits are there?
3 (2)

Are chips one of the words?
yes (no)

What else might you add?
Answers will vary.

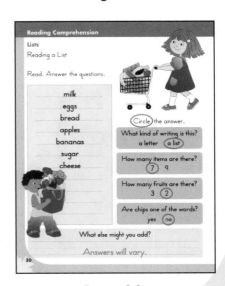

Solutions

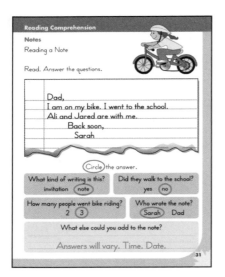

Page 31

Page 32

Page 33

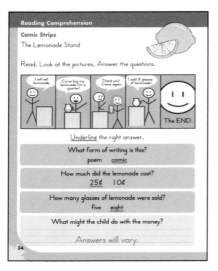

Page 34

Page 35

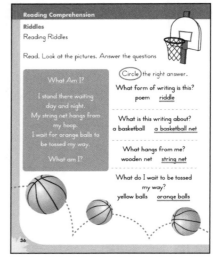

Page 36

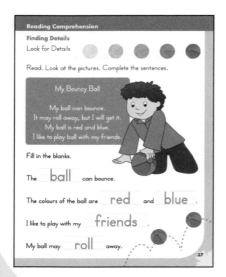

Page 37

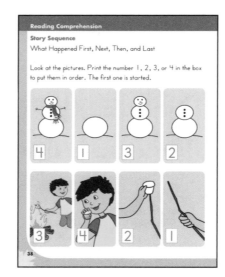

Page 38

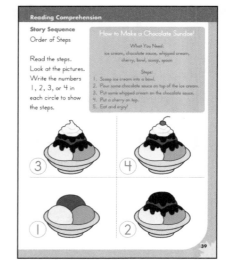

Page 39

Solutions

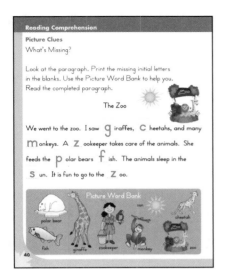

Page 40

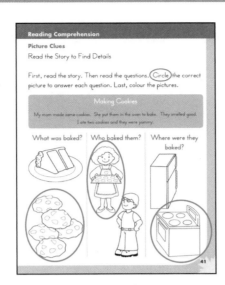

Page 41

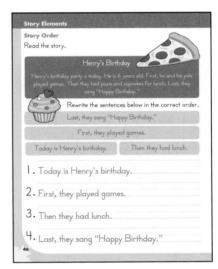

Page 43

Page 44

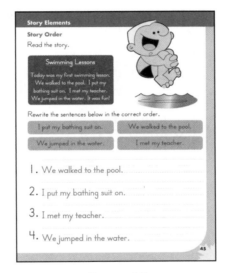

Page 45

Page 46

Page 47

Page 48

Page 50

Solutions

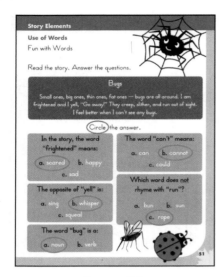

Use of Words

Fun with Words

Read the story. Answer the questions.

Bugs

Small ones, big ones, thin ones, fat ones — bugs are all around. I am frightened and I yell, "Go away!" They creep, slither, and run out of sight. I feel better when I can't see any bugs.

Circle the answer.

In the story, the word "frightened" means:
a. scared   b. happy
c. sad

The word "can't" means:
a. can   b. cannot
c. could

The opposite of "yell" is:
a. sing   b. whisper
c. squeal

Which word does not rhyme with "run"?
a. bun   b. sun
c. rope

The word "bug" is a:
a. noun   b. verb

Page 51

Story Elements

Facts

Finding Facts

Look at the card.
Did you notice the fish bowl?
Can you see the fins?
Do you see the tail?

Answer the questions.

What facts did you learn about the goldfish?

500 types, eat flakes, live in groups

Would you like a goldfish for a pet? Why or why not?

Answers will vary.

Page 53

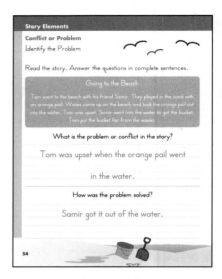

Story Elements

Conflict or Problem

Identify the Problem

Read the story. Answer the questions in complete sentences.

Going to the Beach

Tom went to the beach with his friend Samir. They played in the sand with an orange pail. Waves came up on the beach and took the orange pail out into the water. Tom was upset. Samir went into the water to get the bucket. Tom put the bucket far from the waves.

What is the problem or conflict in the story?

Tom was upset when the orange pail went

in the water.

How was the problem solved?

Samir got it out of the water.

Page 54

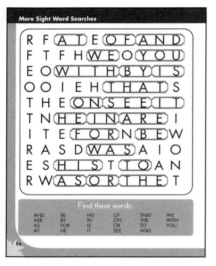

More Sight Word Searches

Find these words:
AND BE HIS OF THAT WE
ARE BY IN IS ON WITH
AS FOR IT OR THE YOU
AT HE SEE TO WAS

Page 56

More Sight Word Searches

Find these words:
ALL COME INTO NO SHE THIS WHEN
AN DO LIKE NOT SO UP
BUT HAD LOOK SAID SOME WERE
CAN HAVE MY SAW THEY WHAT

Page 57

More Sight Word Searches

Find these words:
AM DOWN HER LITTLE THEM WANT WOULD
CAME GET HERE MAKE THEN WENT YES
COULD GO IF OUT THERE WILL

Page 58

64